Pupil's Book

Recorder *from the* Beginning

All Together Christmas R

Arranged by John Pitts

Containing 17 Christmas carols, this book enables beginner recorder players to perform simplified arrangements of popular seasonal repertoire either on their own, using the various accompaniment options to provide the full, original melody, or alongside singers and more advanced players.

The familiar melody lines of these festive favourites are accompanied by two counter-melodies, each employing the same rhythm as the original whilst requiring a knowledge of only three or five notes and thus catering for recorder players of all abilities—Part 1 uses only the notes G, A and B and is therefore suitable for players who have reached page 12 in *Recorder from the Beginning Book 1*; Part 2 uses the notes D, E, G, A and B and is therefore suitable for players who have reached page 26 in the aforementioned method. Wherever possible the two harmony parts, which can be used simultaneously, include sections of the original melody giving the beginner points of familiarity and reassurance. The arrangements are ordered in respect of the note range of the original tunes.

Both the backing tracks and piano accompaniments, the latter available to download free from www.hybridpublications.com using the registration code printed on page 2, incorporate the original carol melody. Both also assume each carol is to be played twice through (unless indicated otherwise) with introductions to the first verse and 'links' into the second, the lengths of which are specified at the head of each carol. Words are also included enabling singers to take part in the performances, as are guitar chord symbols.

This book comes as a response to the countless requests I have received from teachers for simplified arrangements of carols; I hope it meets their needs, enabling even beginner recorder players to enjoy joining in the Christmas celebrations.

John Pitts

Chester Music Limited
(part of The Music Sales Group)
14/15 Berners Street, London W1T 3LJ

Piano accompaniments for each of the 17 carols
are available as free bonus material,
downloadable to your computer.
Visit: www.hybridpublications.com
Registration is free and easy.
Your registration code is AH445.

Arranged by John Pitts.
Music processed by Paul Ewers Music Design.
Edited by Fiona Bolton.

Printed in the EU.

Contents

Good King Wenceslas

Words by J. M. Neale
Music: Traditional

CD Track 02
Intro: 5 bars
Link: 3 bars

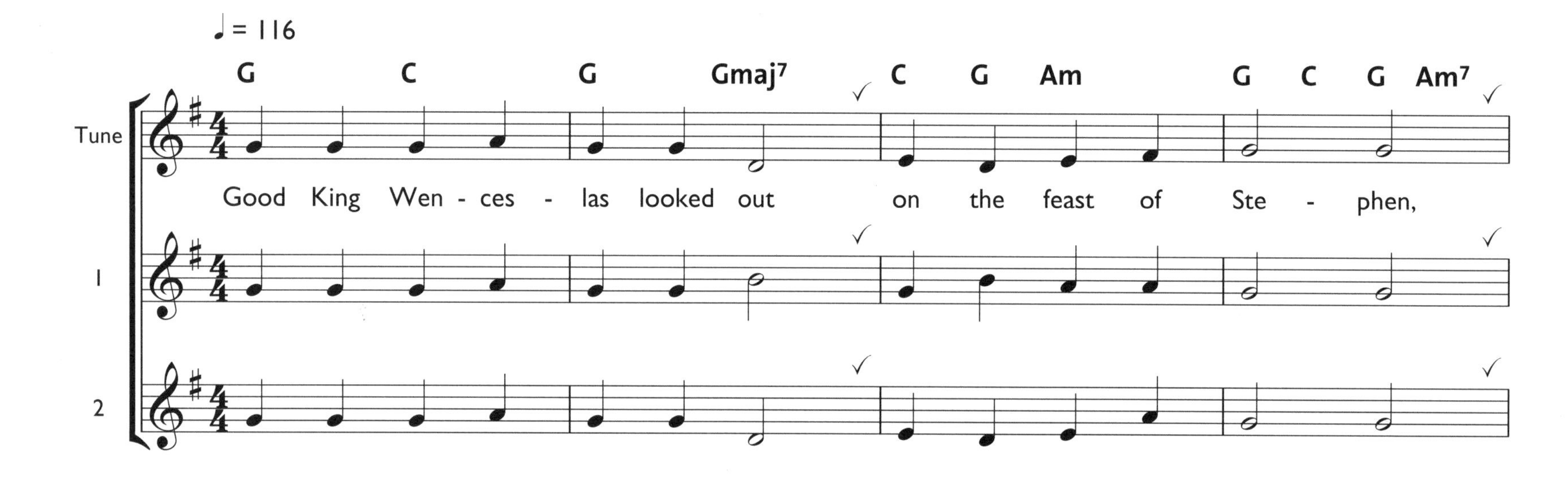

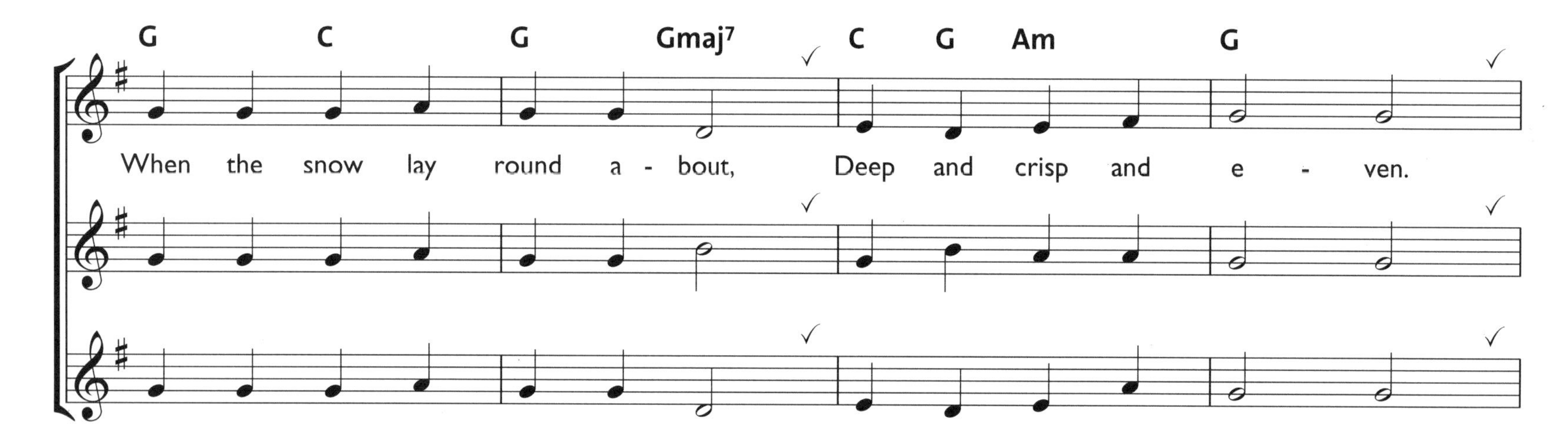

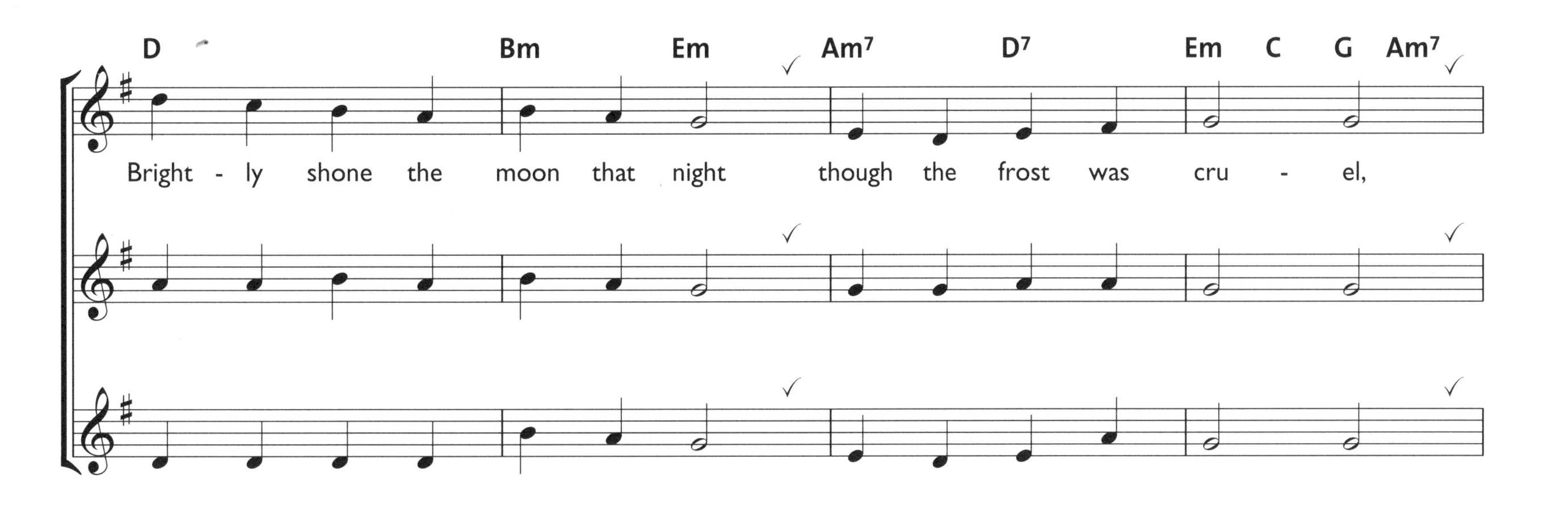
D
Bm
Em
Am7
D7
Em C G Am7
Bright - ly shone the moon that night though the frost was cru - el,

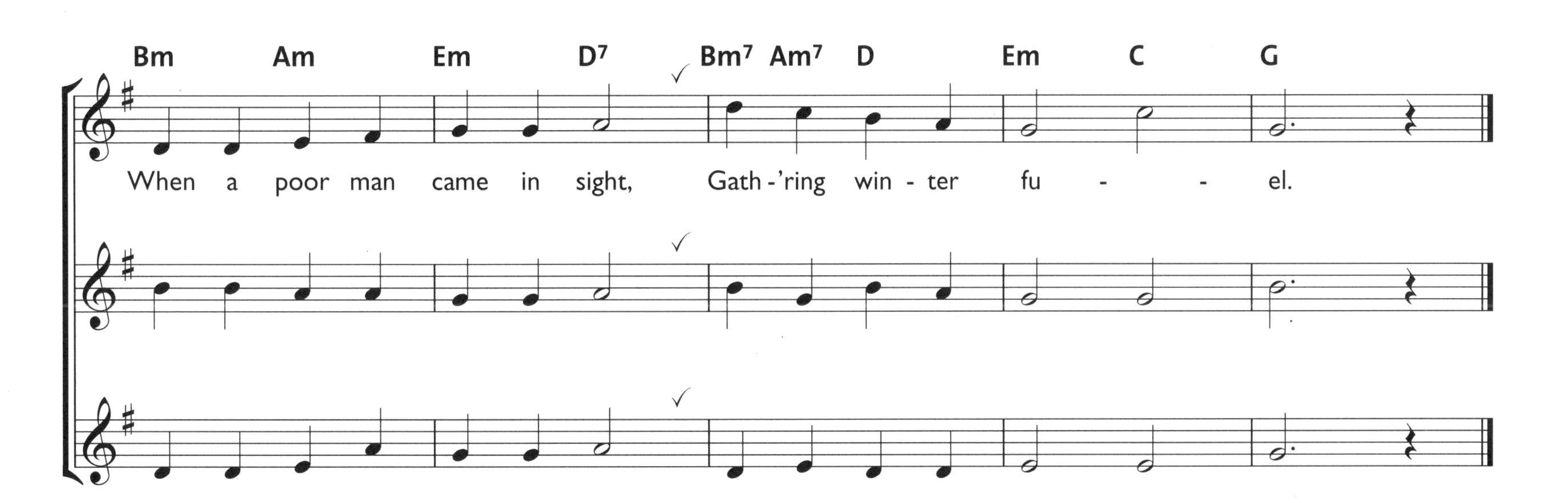
Bm Am Em D7 Bm7 Am7 D Em C G
When a poor man came in sight, Gath-'ring win - ter fu - - el.

Infant Holy, Infant Lowly

Traditional Polish Carol
English Translation by Edith M. Reed

CD Track 03
Intro: 4 bars
Link: 2 bars

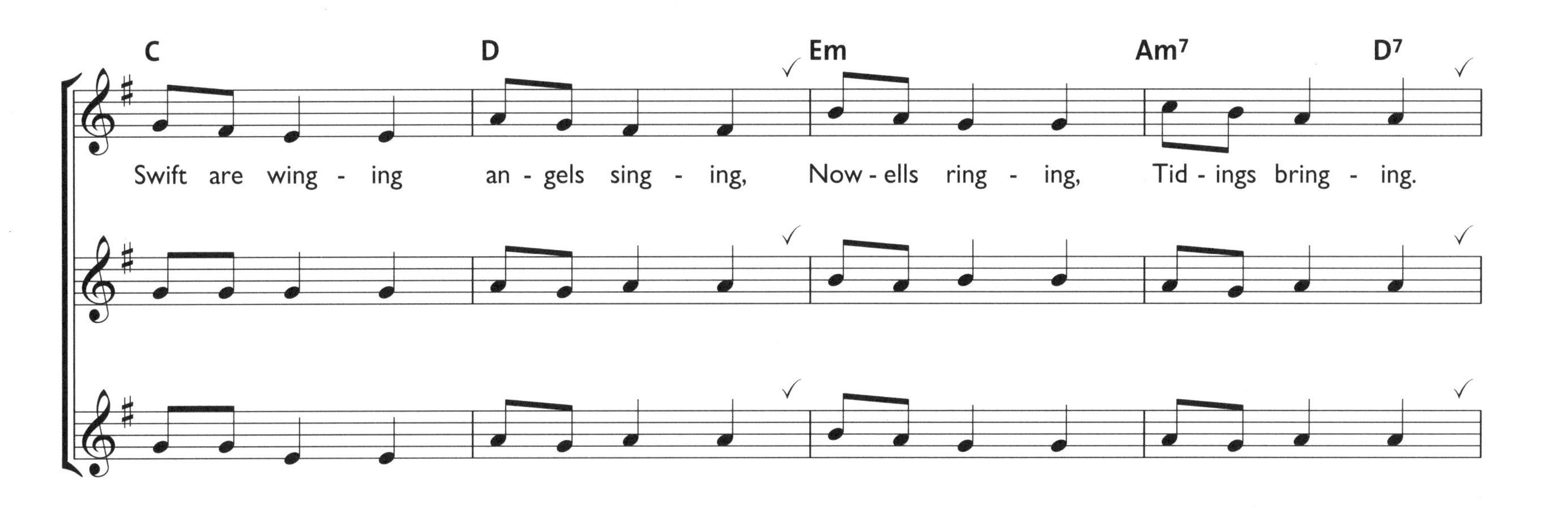
C
D
Em
Am7
D7
Swift are wing - ing an - gels sing - ing, Now - ells ring - ing, Tid - ings bring - ing.

Gmaj7
D7
Em7
Em
G
Am
D
G
Christ the babe is Lord of all, Christ the babe is Lord of all.

I Saw Three Ships

Traditional

CD Track 04
Intro: 4 bars
Link: 4 bars

Mary Had A Baby

Traditional Afro-American Spiritual

CD Track 05
Intro: 4 bars
Link: 2 bars

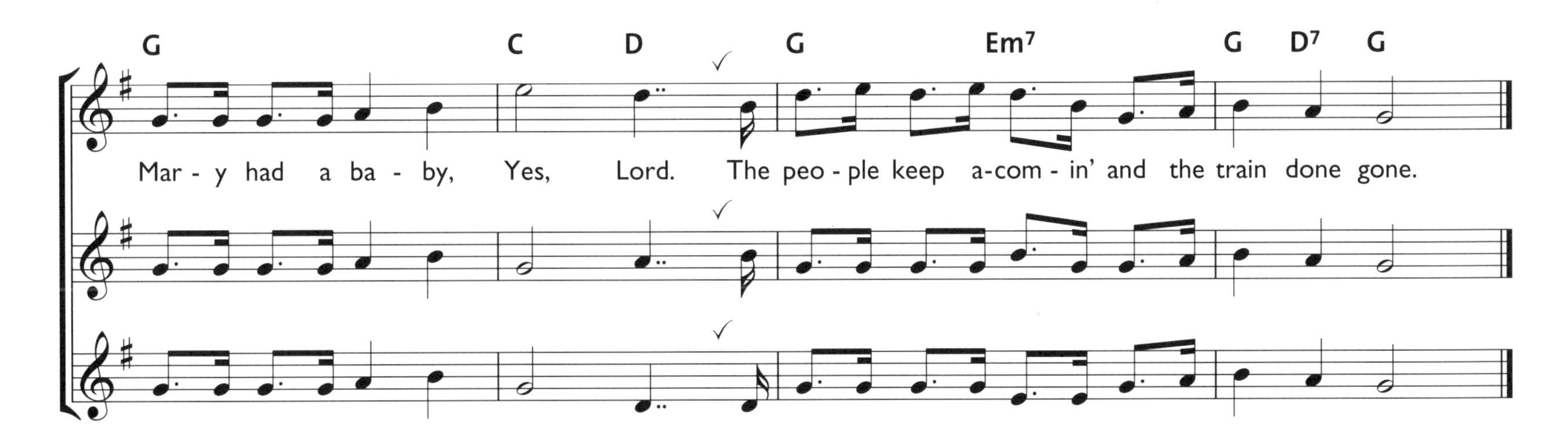

We Three Kings

Words & Music by John Henry Hopkins

CD Track 06
Intro: 8 bars
Link: 4 bars

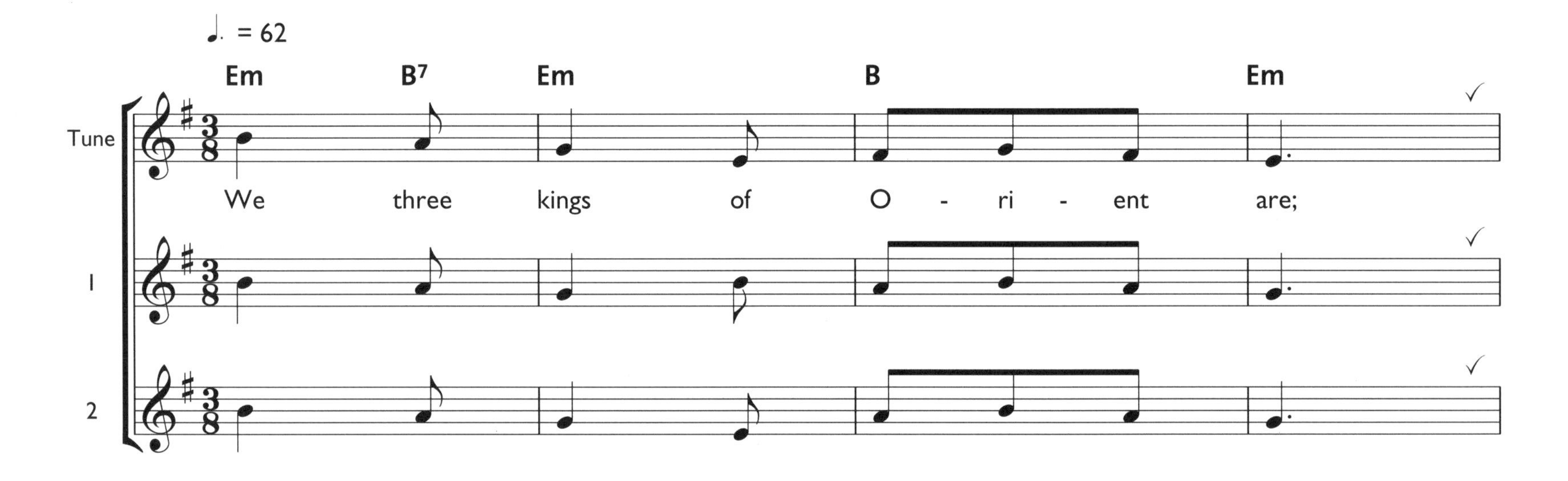

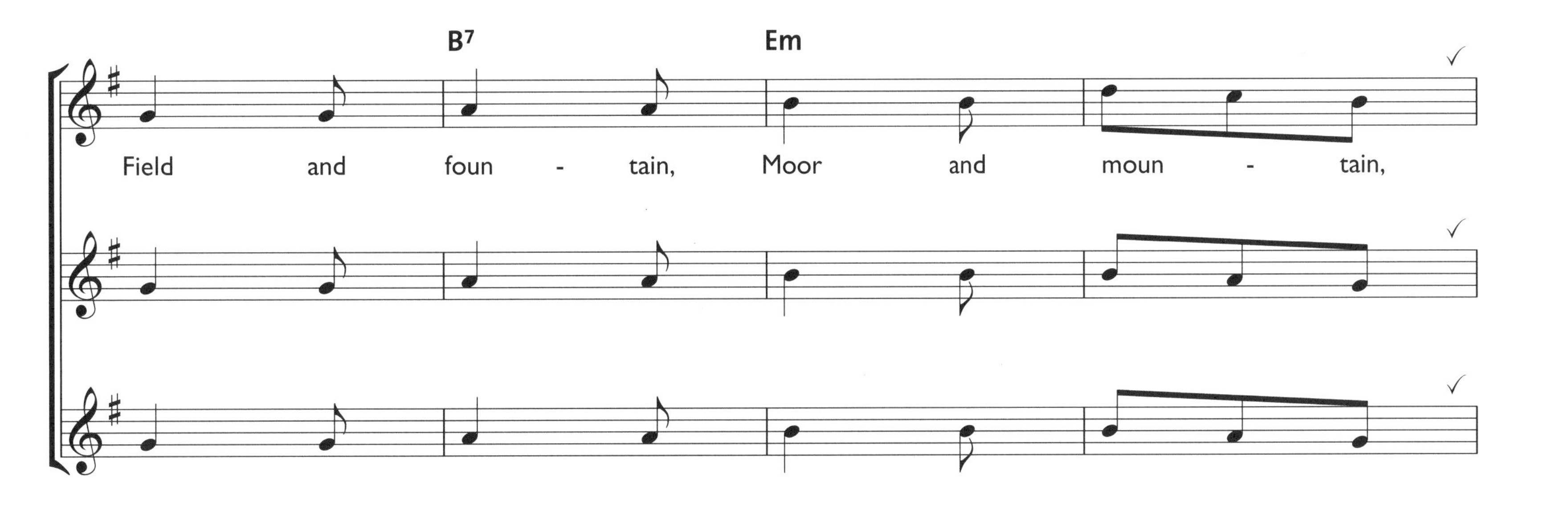
B7
Em
Field and foun - tain, Moor and moun - tain,

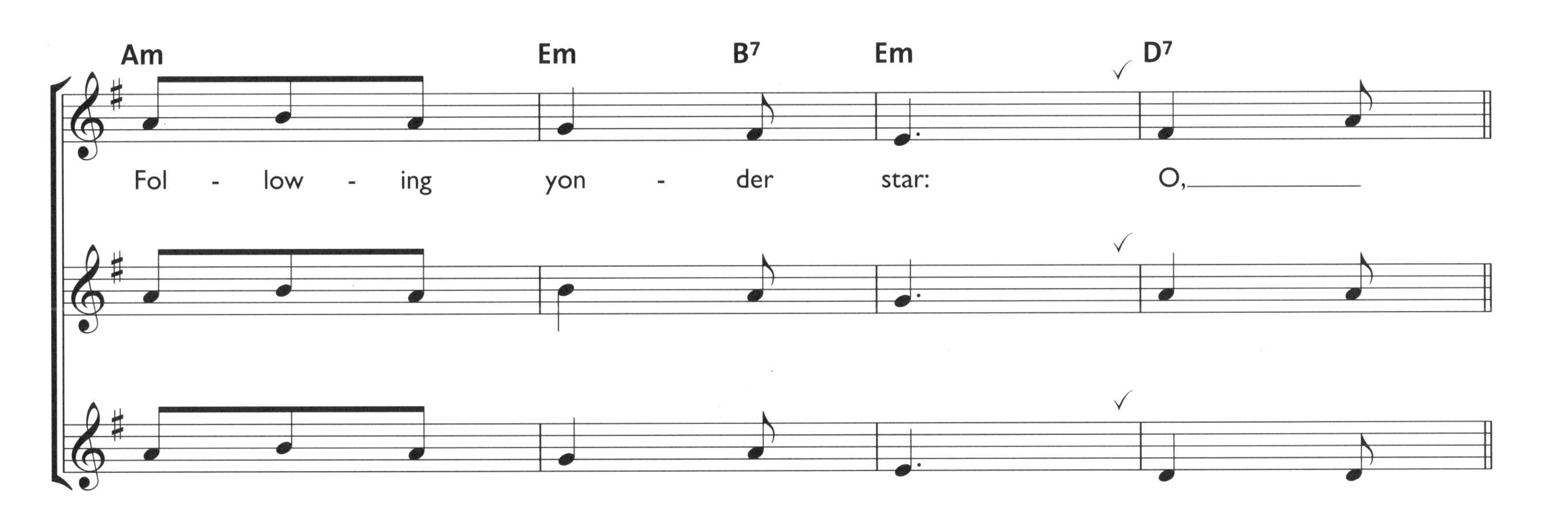
Am
Em
B7
Em
D7
Fol - low - ing yon - der star: O,

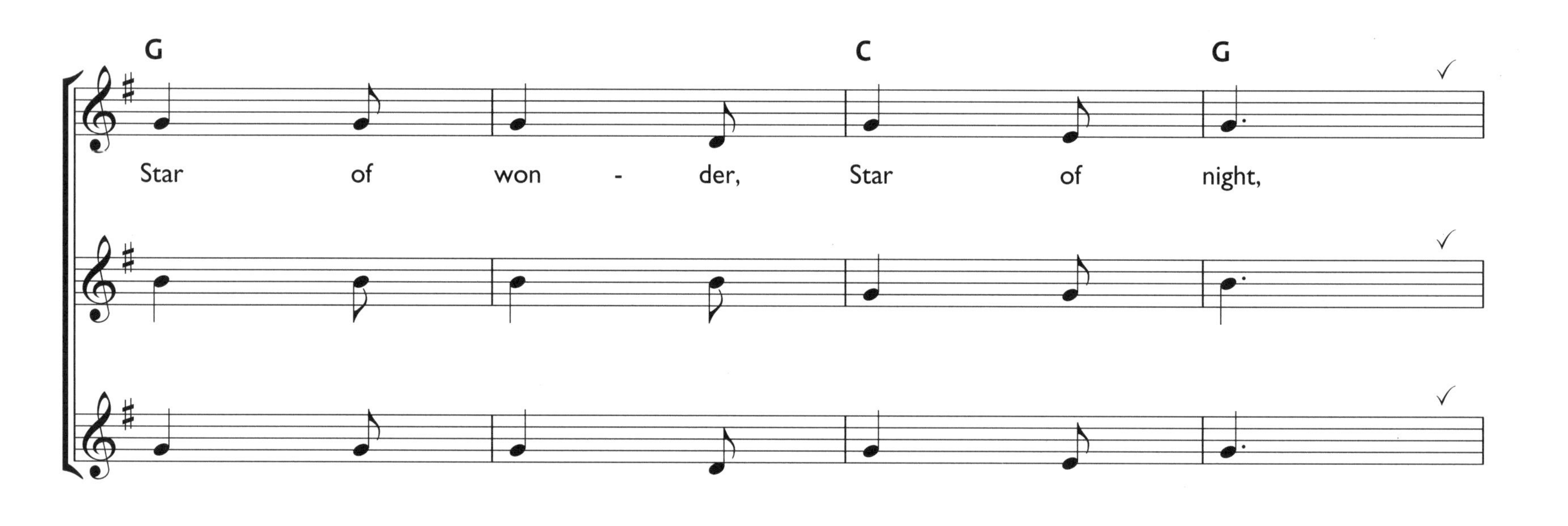
G
C
G
Star of won - der, Star of night,

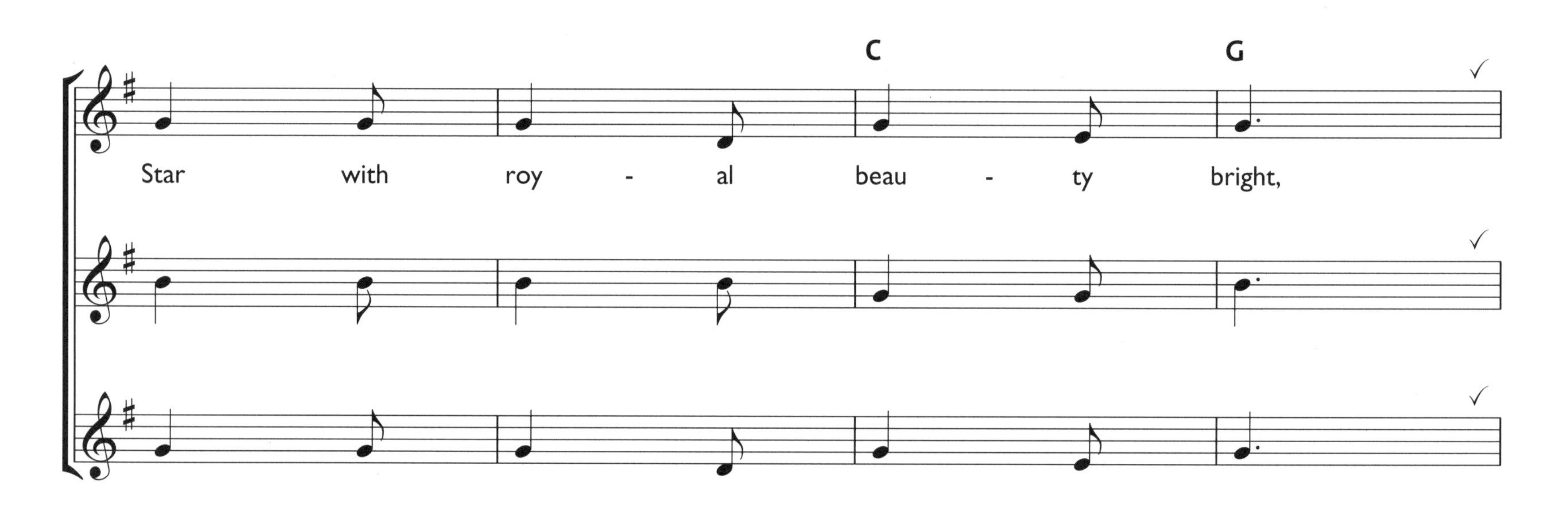
C
G
Star with roy - al beau - ty bright,

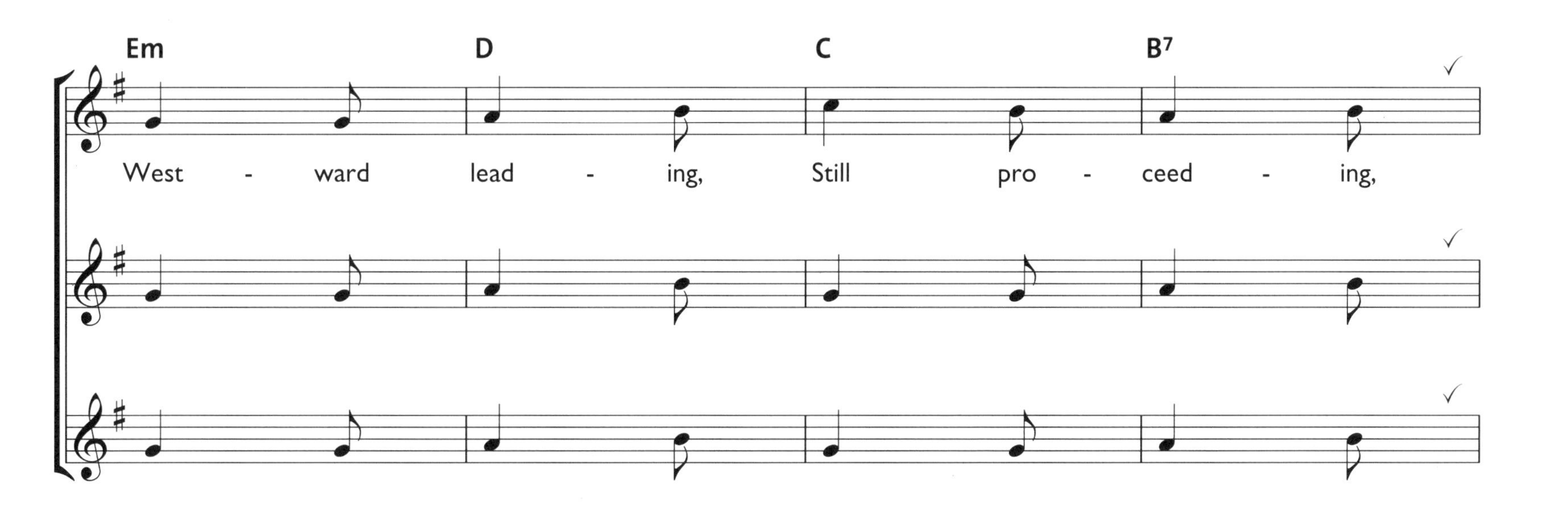
Em
D
C
B7
West - ward lead - ing, Still pro - ceed - ing,

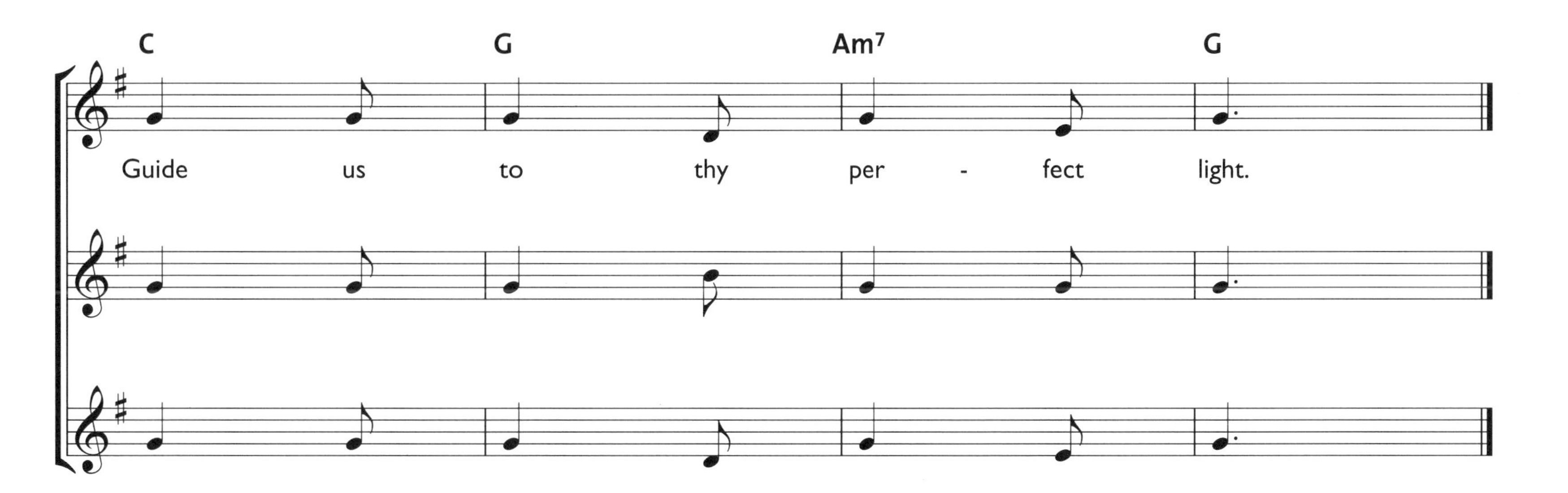
C
G
Am7
G
Guide us to thy per - fect light.

O Come All Ye Faithful

Words & Music by John Francis Wade & William Thomas Brooke

CD Track 07
Intro: 4 bars
Link: 4 bars
(Play bracketed notes 1° only)

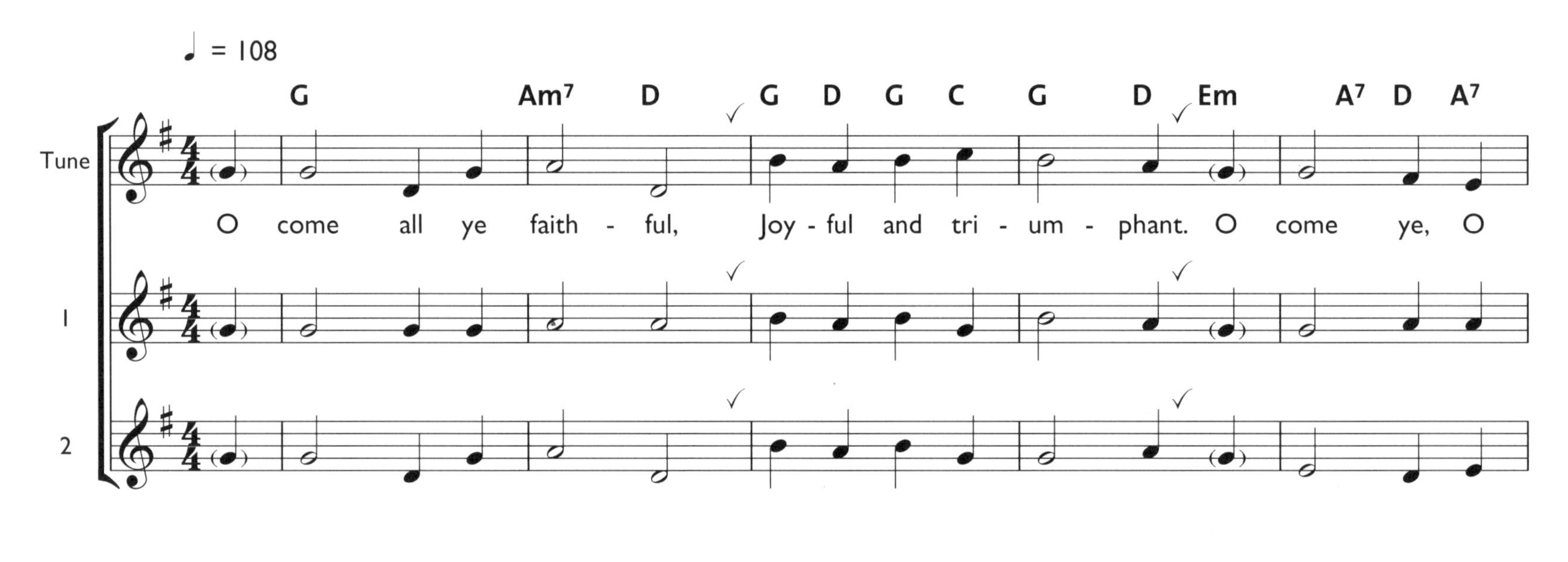

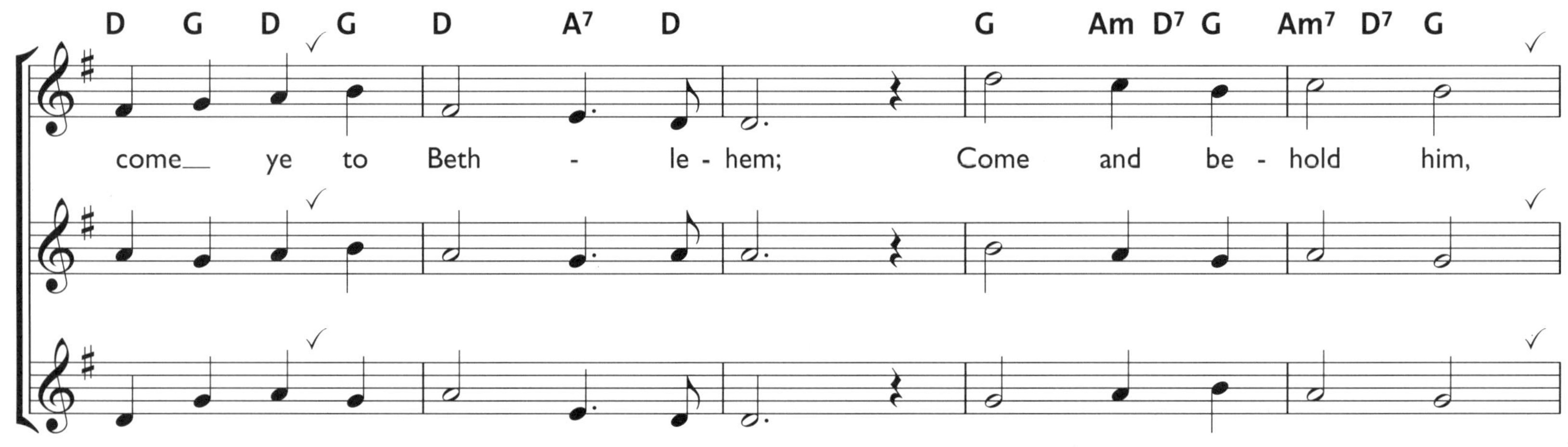

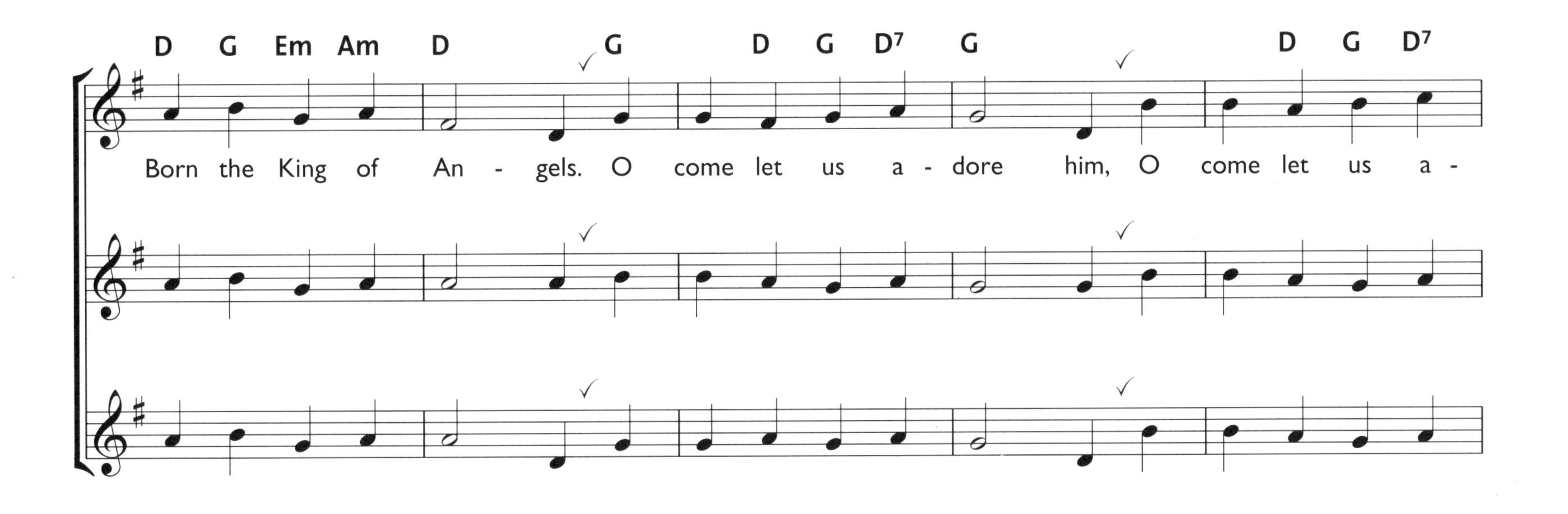
D G Em Am D G D G D7 G D G D7
Born the King of An - gels. O come let us a - dore him, O come let us a -

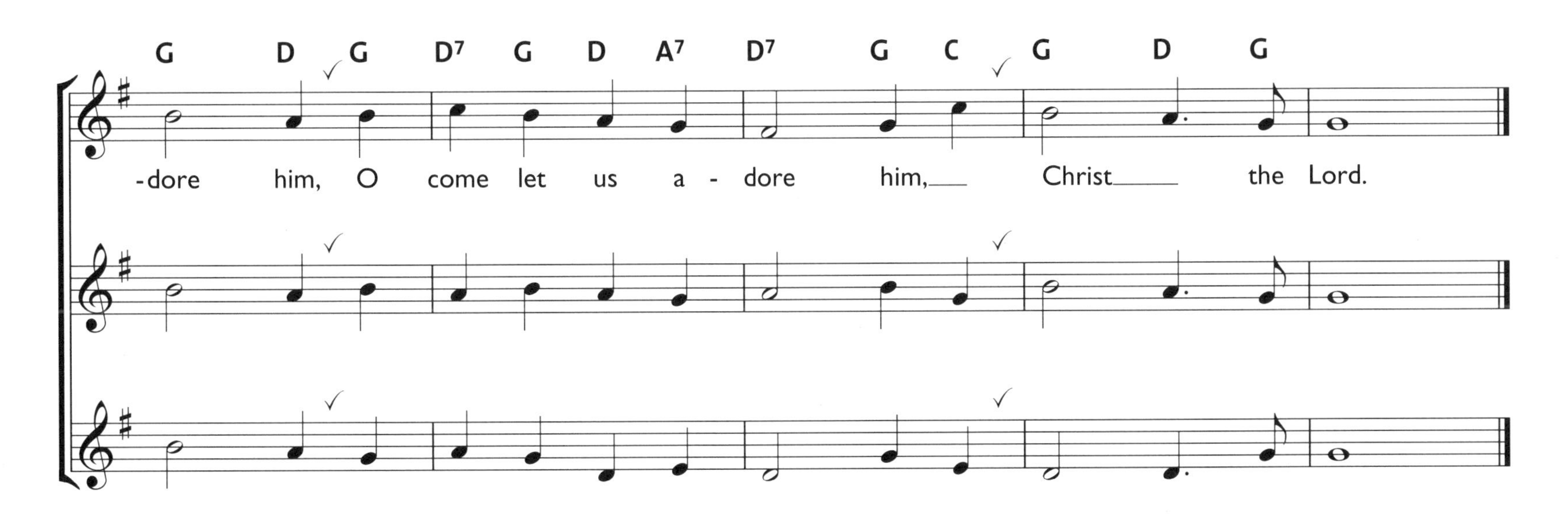
G D G D7 G D A7 D7 G C G D G
-dore him, O come let us a - dore him, Christ the Lord.

The Holly And The Ivy

Traditional

CD Track 08
Intro: 4 bars
Link: 4 bars

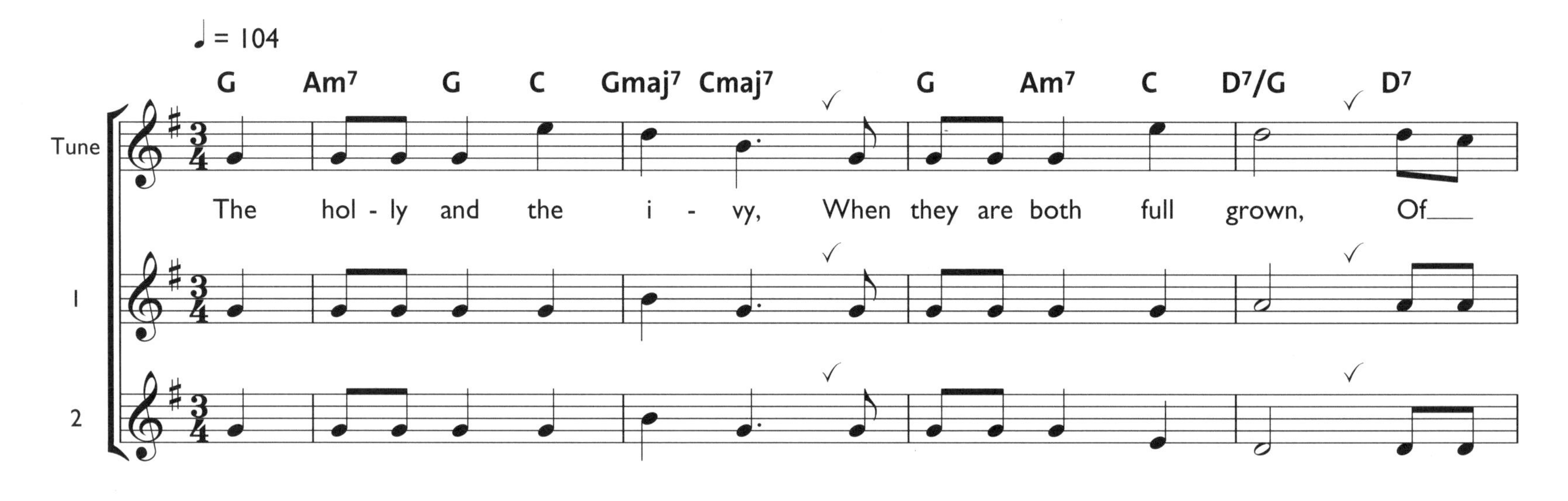

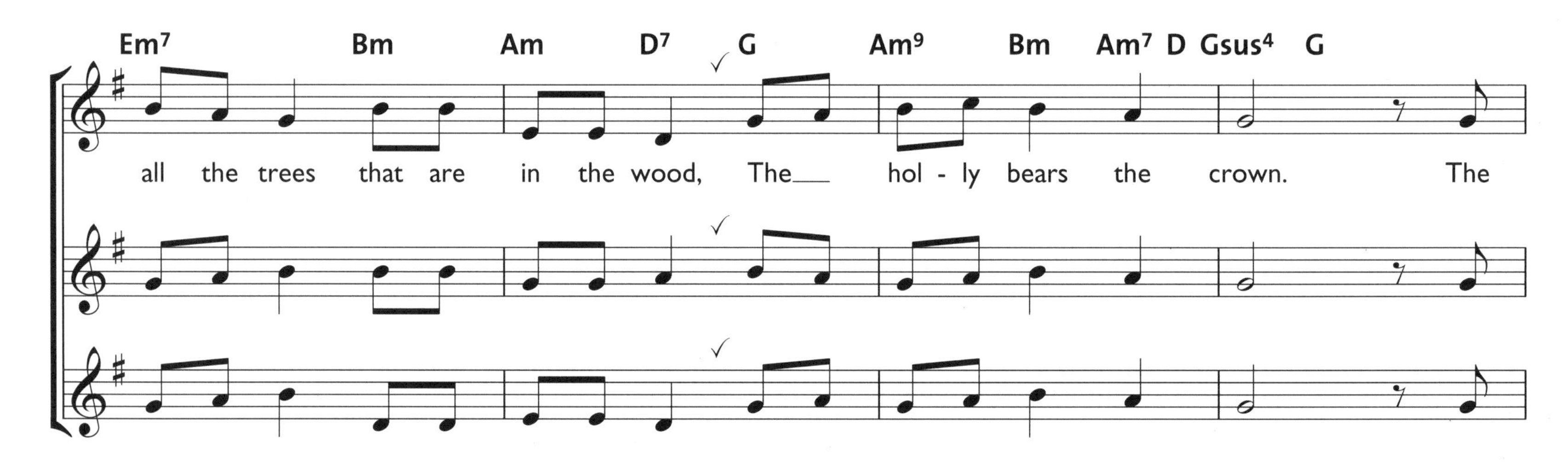

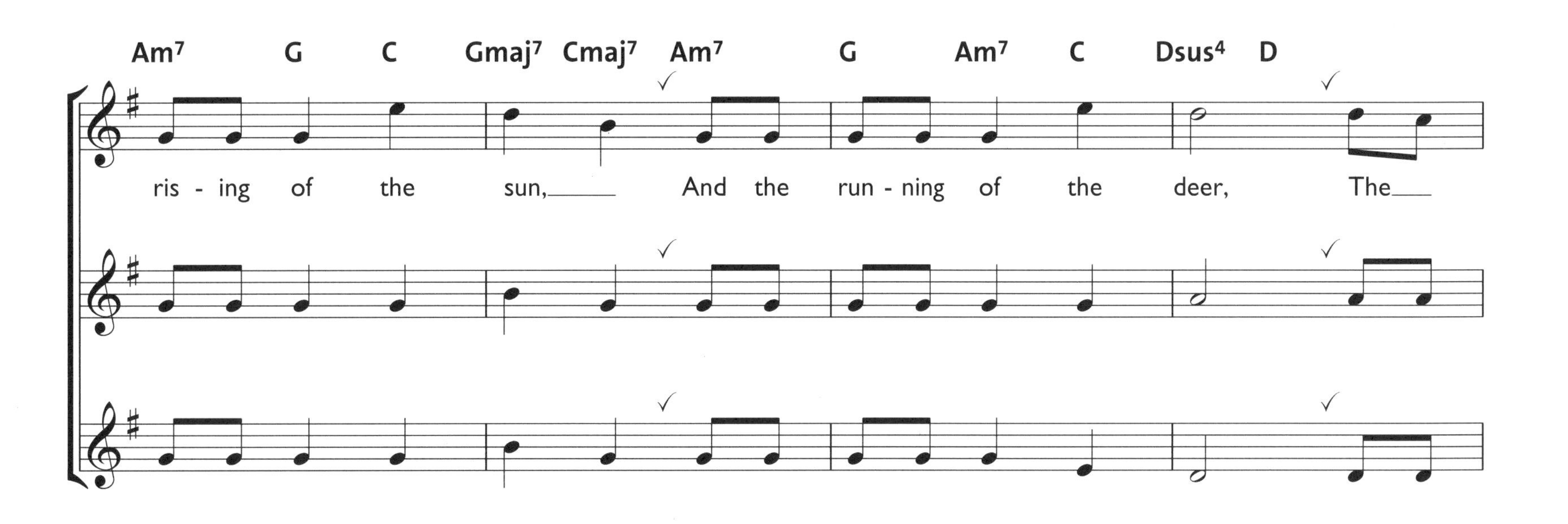
Am7 G C Gmaj7 Cmaj7 Am7 G Am7 C Dsus4 D
ris - ing of the sun,___ And the run - ning of the deer, The___

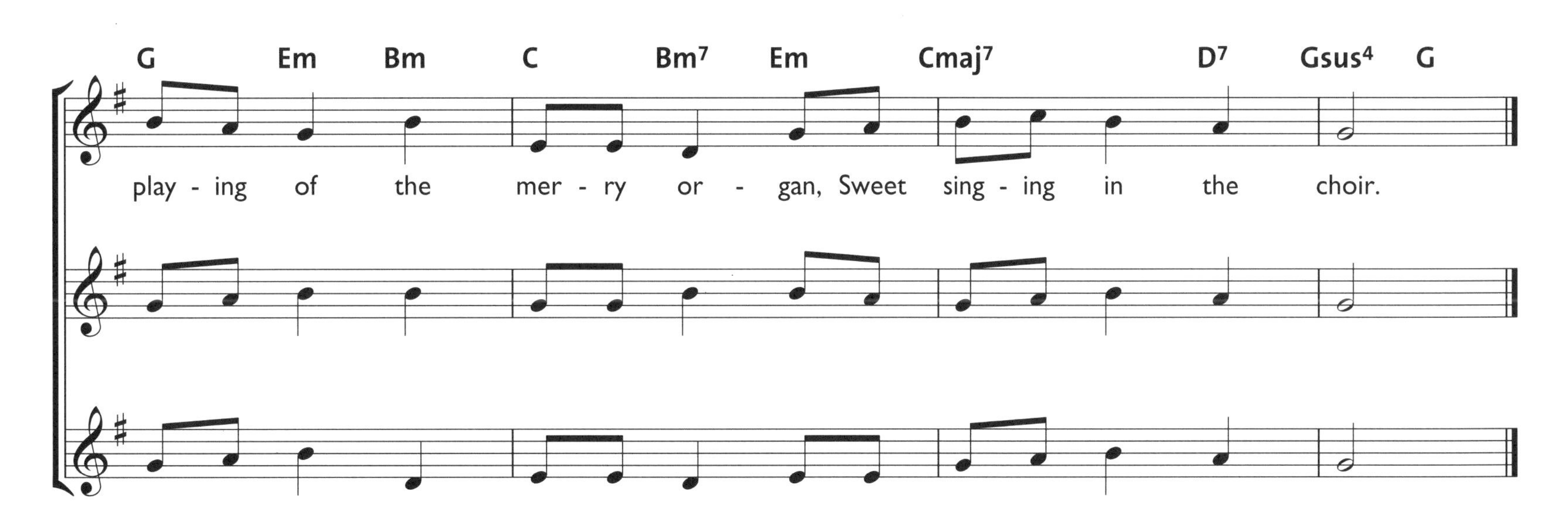
G Em Bm C Bm7 Em Cmaj7 D7 Gsus4 G
play - ing of the mer - ry or - gan, Sweet sing - ing in the choir.

Jingle Bells

Words & Music by J. S. Pierpont

CD Track 09
Intro: 4 bars
D.C. al Fine (no link)

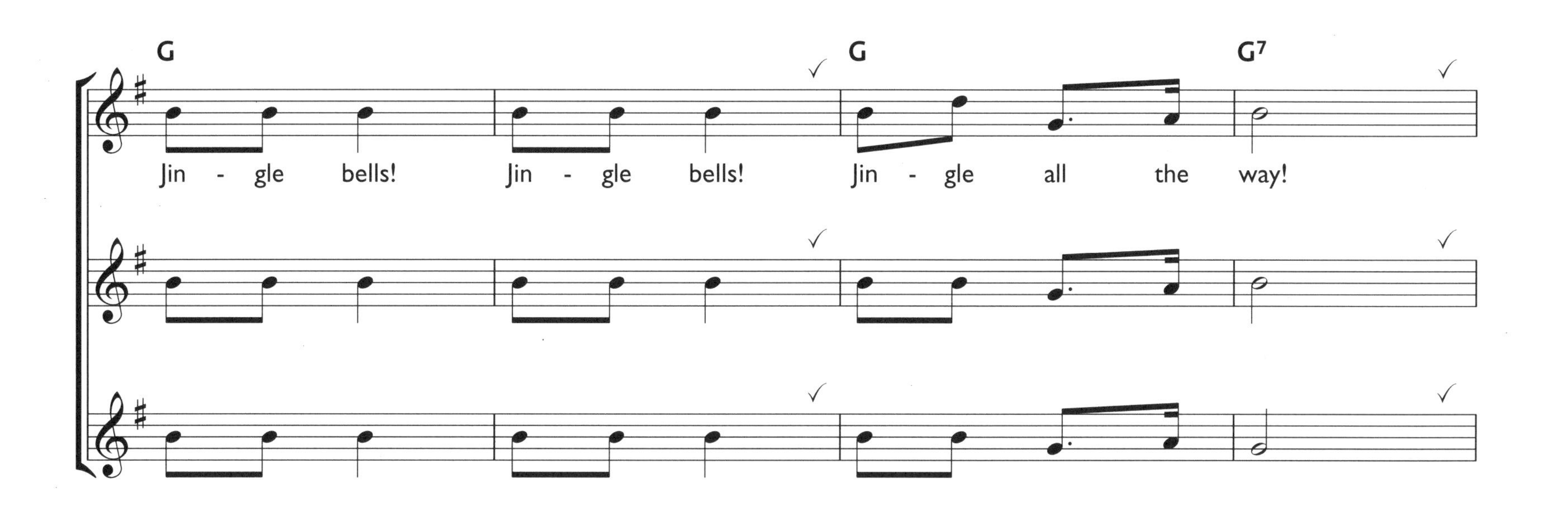
G
G
G7
Jin - gle bells! Jin - gle bells! Jin - gle all the way!

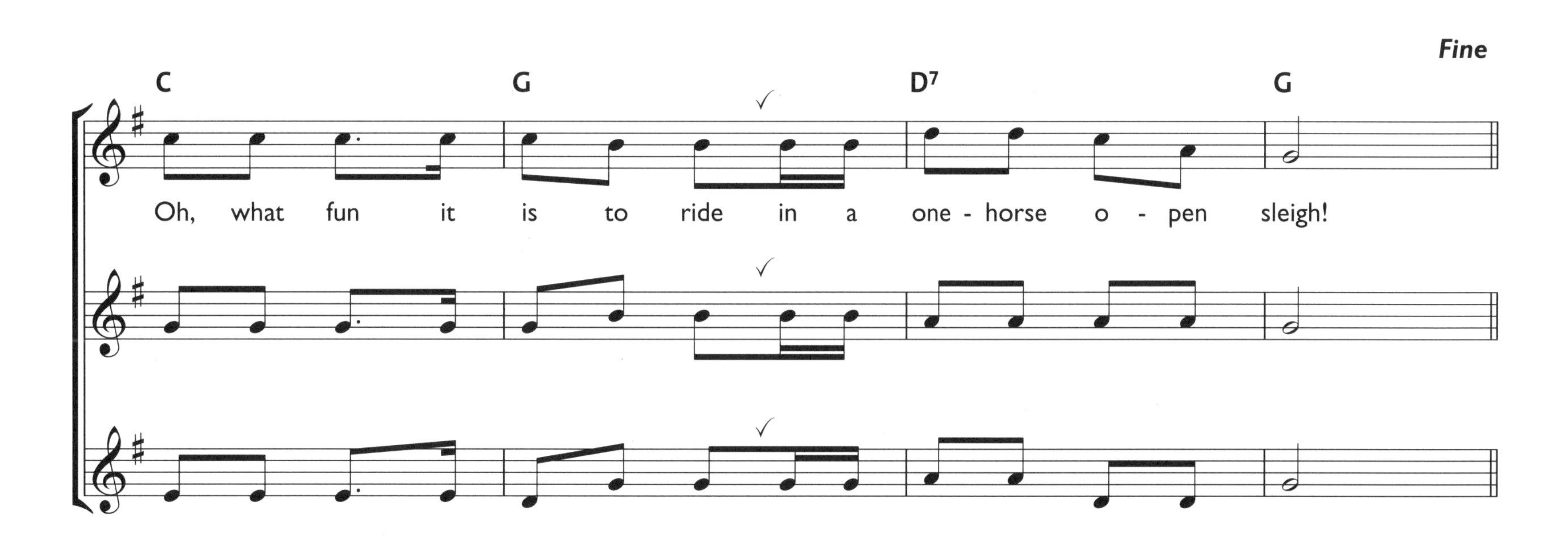
Fine
C
G
D7
G
Oh, what fun it is to ride in a one - horse o - pen sleigh!

G
C
Dash - ing through the snow in a one - horse o - pen sleigh,

Am
D
D7
G
O'er the fields we go, Laugh - ing all the way!

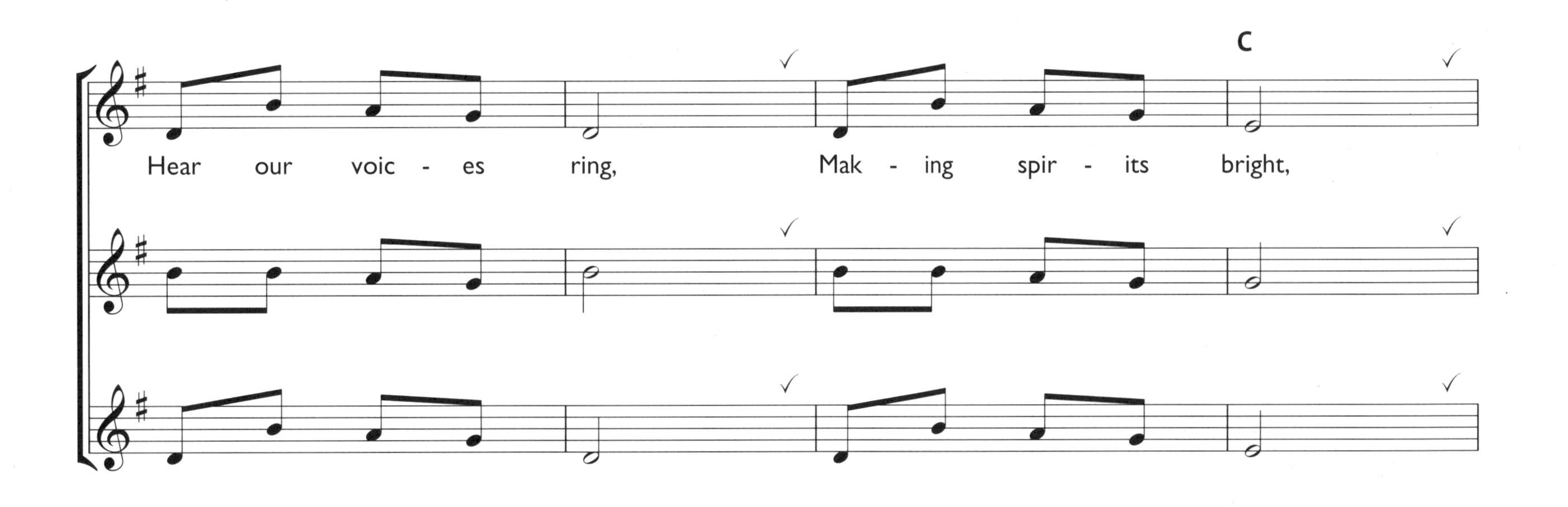
C
Hear our voic - es ring,
Mak - ing spir - its bright,

Am
G
D7
G
D.C. al Fine
O what fun it is to sing a sleigh - ing song to - night.

Away In A Manger

Words: Traditional
Music by William Kirkpatrick

CD Track 10
Intro: 4 bars
Link: 4 bars

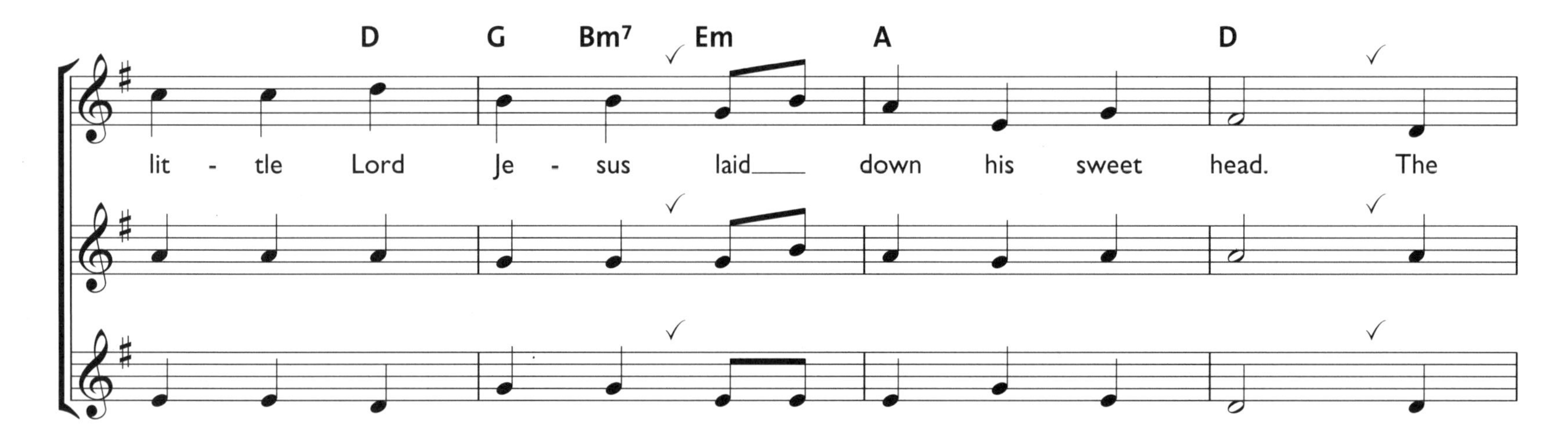

G
Am7
Bm
G
Em
Am
stars in the bright sky looked down where he lay, The

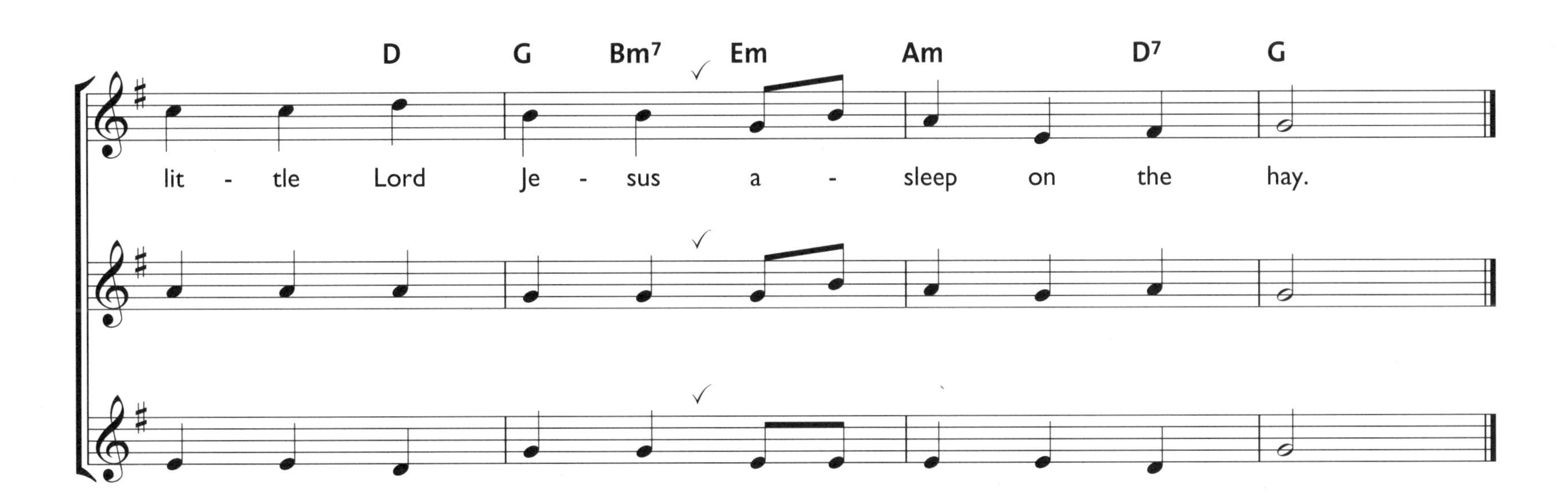
D
G
Bm7
Em
Am
D7
G
lit - tle Lord Je - sus a - sleep on the hay.

Once In Royal David's City

Words by Cecil Alexander
Music by Henry Gauntlett

CD Track 11
Intro: 4 bars
Link: 2 bars

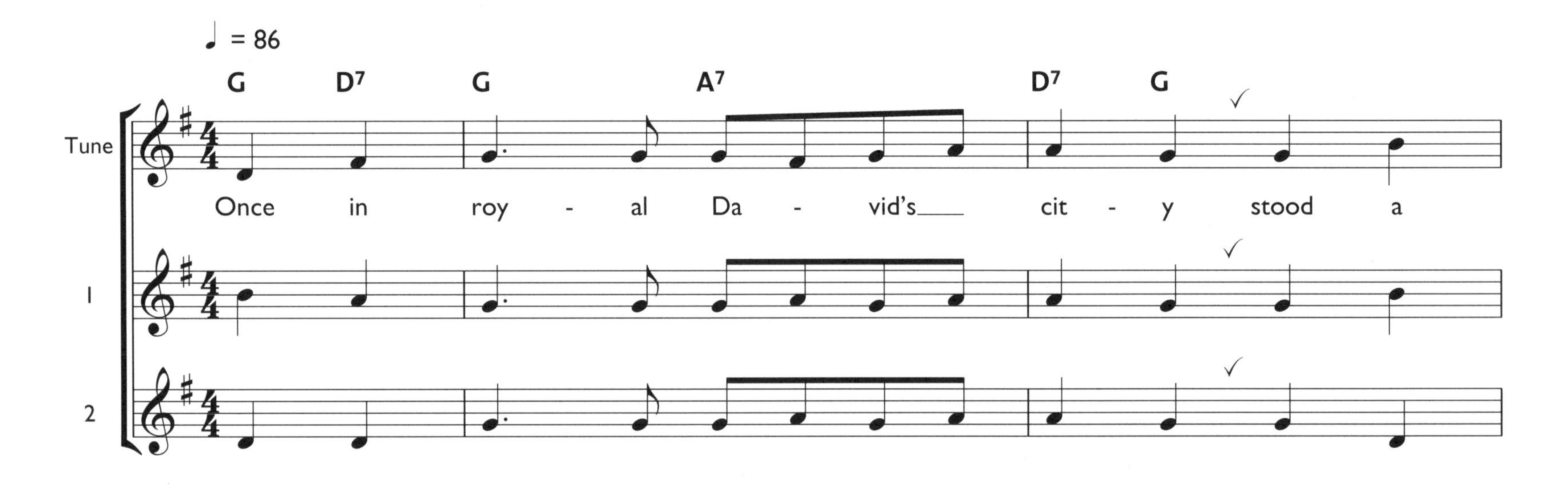

D7 G D G Am G D G C
ba - by in a man - ger for his bed. Mar - y

G Am D7 G C G Am G D G
was that moth - er mild, Je - sus Christ her lit - tle child.

Hark! The Herald Angels Sing

Words by Charles Wesley
Music by Felix Mendelssohn

CD Track 12
Intro: 4 bars
Link: 4 bars

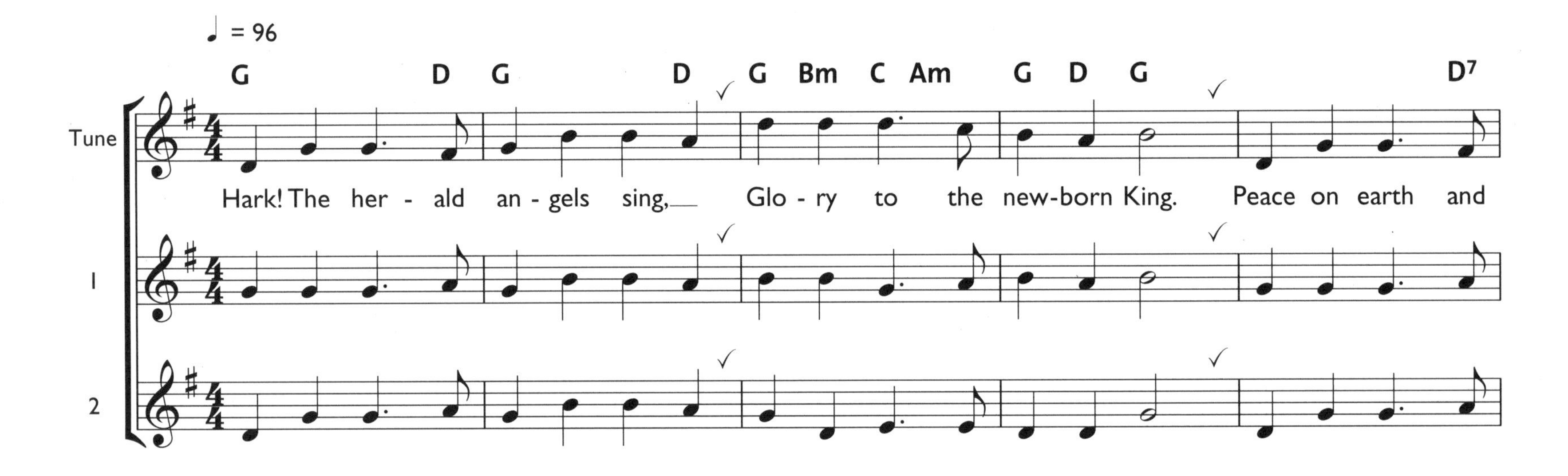

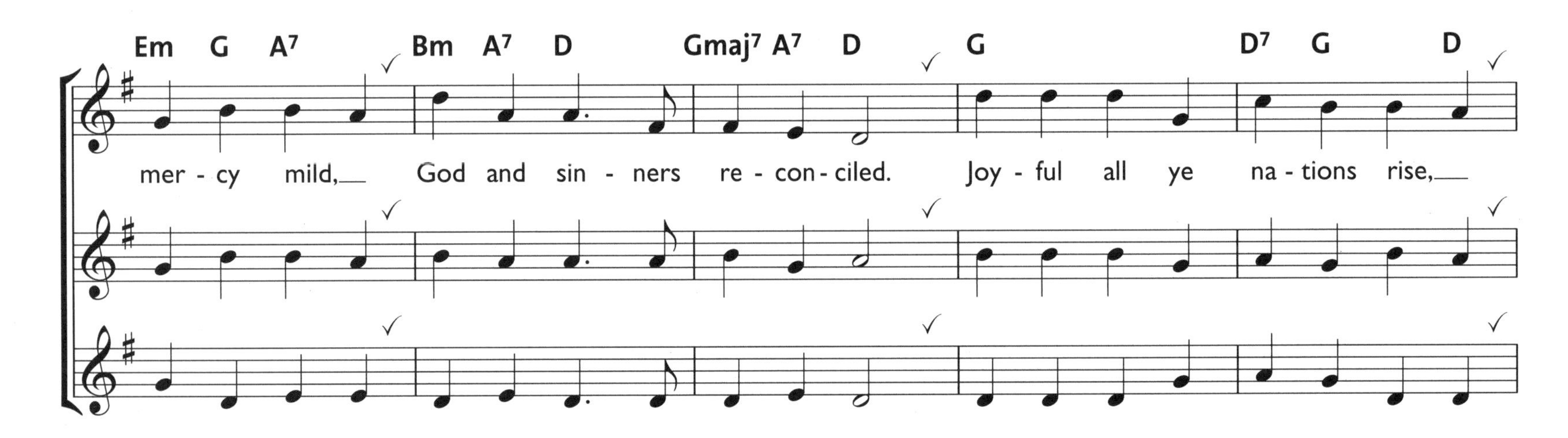

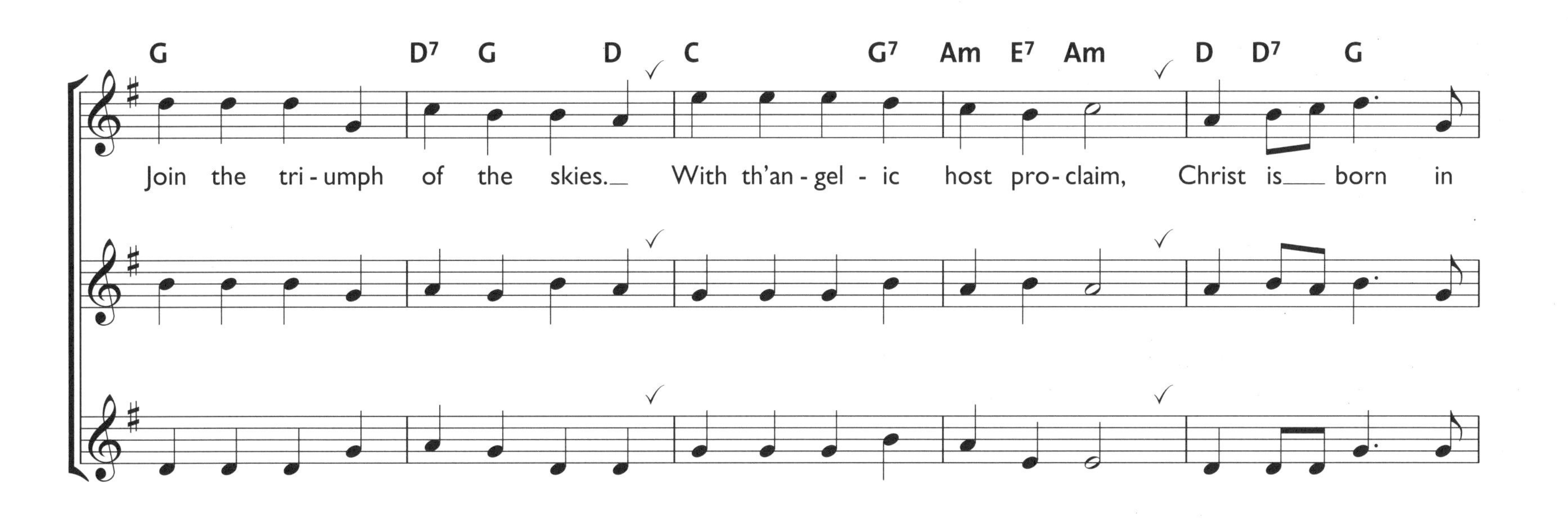
G D7 G D C G7 Am E7 Am D D7 G
Join the tri - umph of the skies. With th'an - gel - ic host pro - claim, Christ is born in

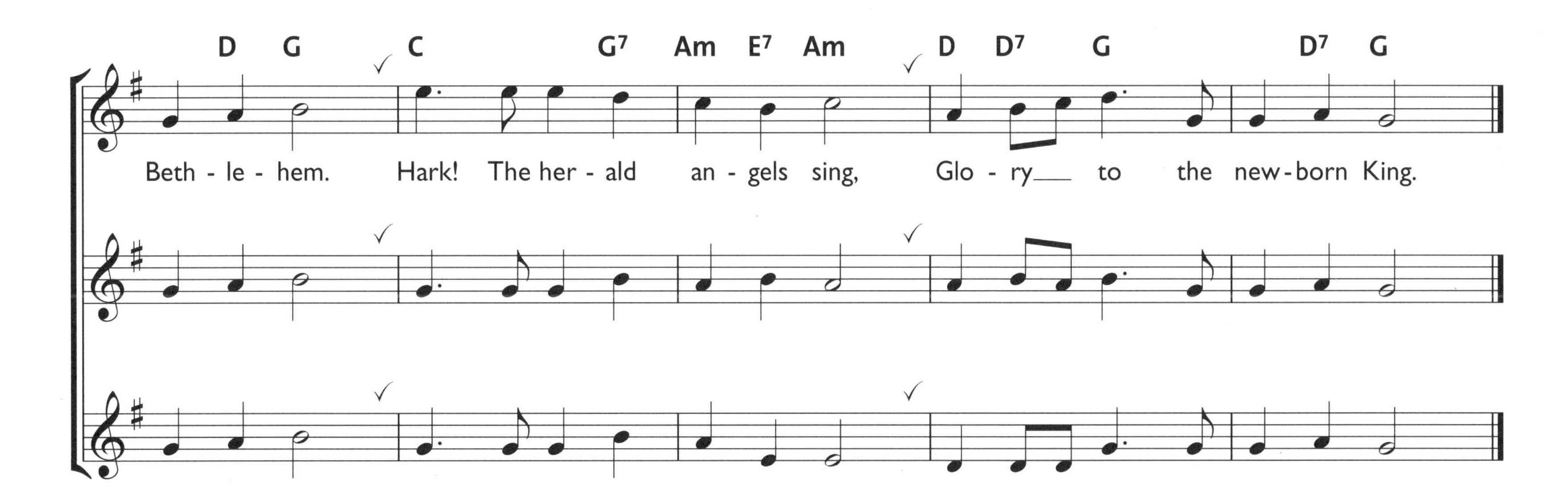
D G C G7 Am E7 Am D D7 G D7 G
Beth - le - hem. Hark! The her - ald an - gels sing, Glo - ry to the new - born King.

Past Three O'Clock

Words by George Ratcliffe Woodward
Music: Traditional

CD Track 13
Intro: 4 bars
D.C. x 2 al Fine (no link)

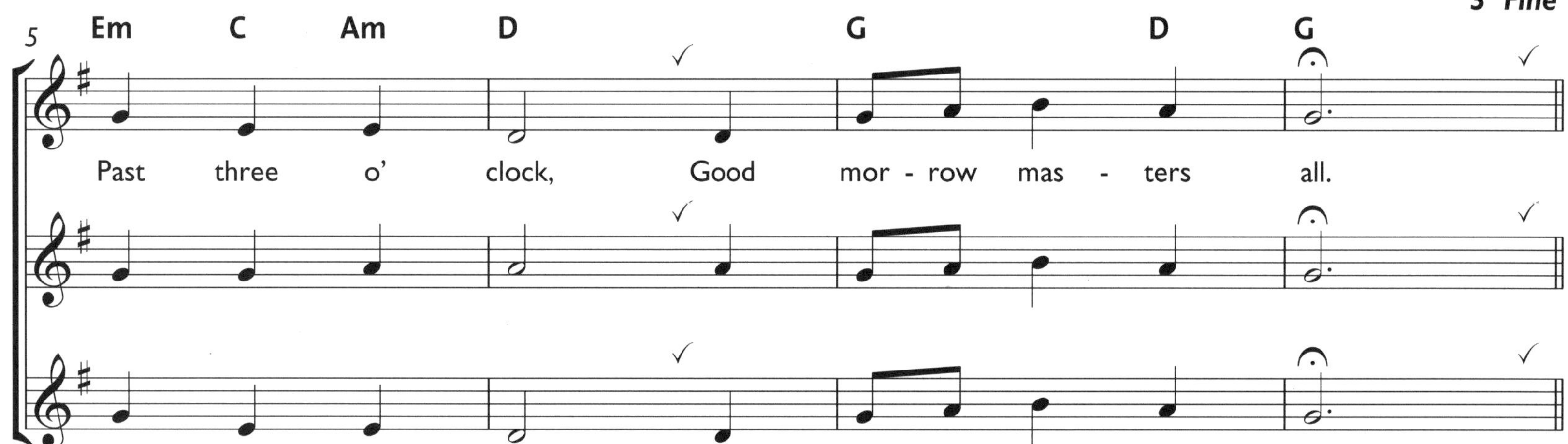

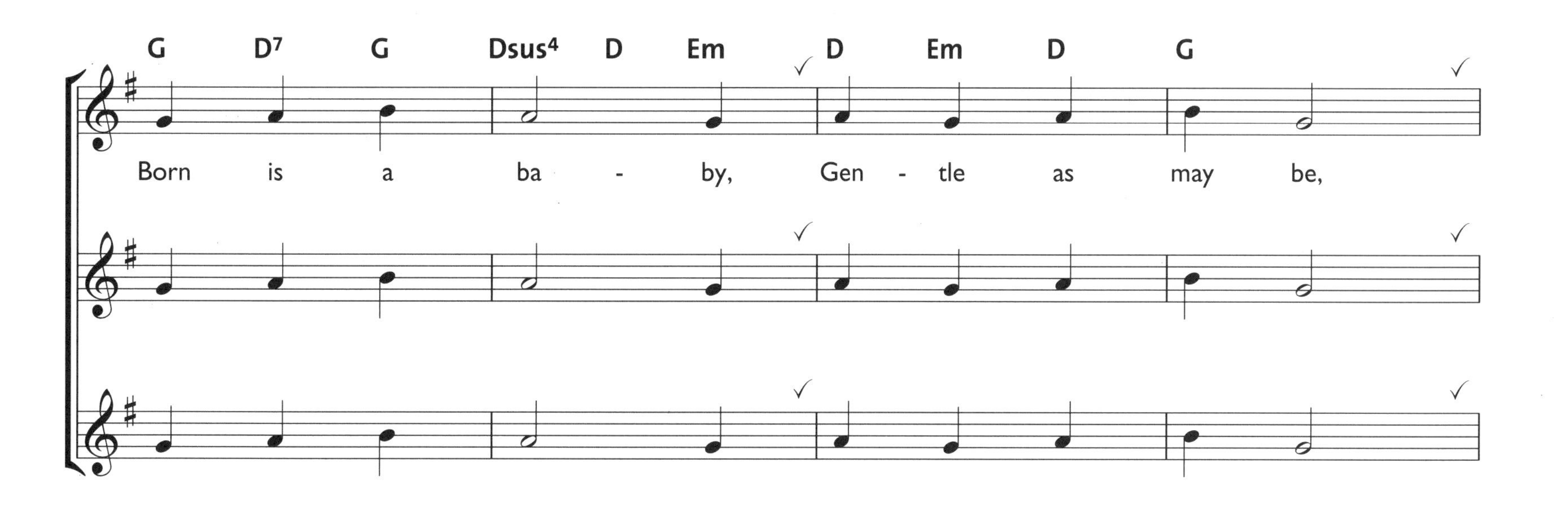
G D7 G Dsus4 D Em D Em D G
Born is a ba - by, Gen - tle as may be,

D.C. x 2 al Fine
Em C Dsus4 D Em D Em D G C
Son of th' e - ter - nal Fa - ther su - per - nal.

In The Bleak Midwinter

Words by Christina Rossetti
Music by Gustav Holst

CD Track 14
Intro: 4 bars
Link: 4 bars

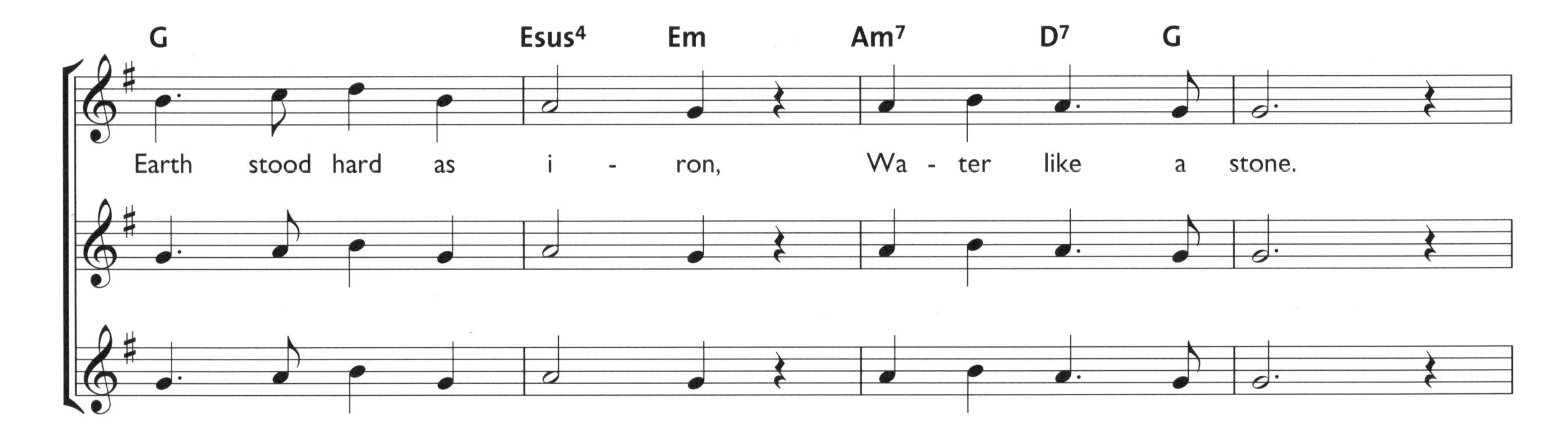

C G C G7 C Em G Bm Am Cmaj7 D
Snow had fal - len, snow on snow, Snow on snow.

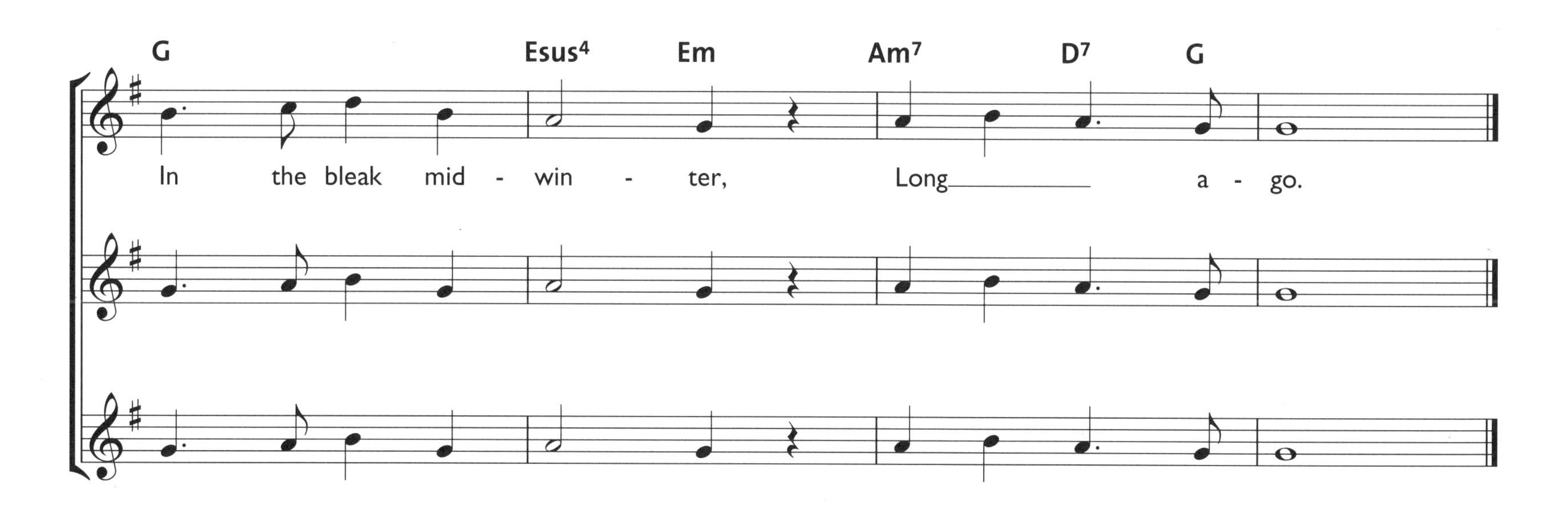
G Esus4 Em Am7 D7 G
In the bleak mid - win - ter, Long a - go.

The Virgin Mary Had A Baby Boy

Traditional

CD Track 15
Intro: 2 bars
Link: 2 bars

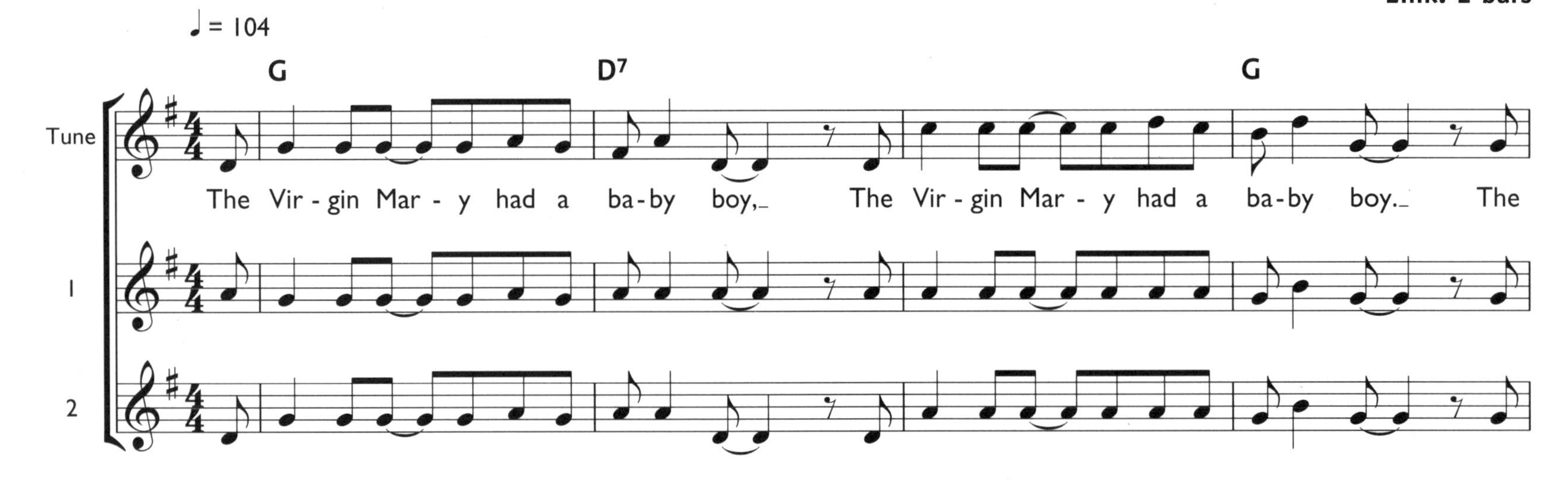

G D7 Em D7 G D7 G
He came_ from the glo - ry, He came from the glor - ious king - dom.

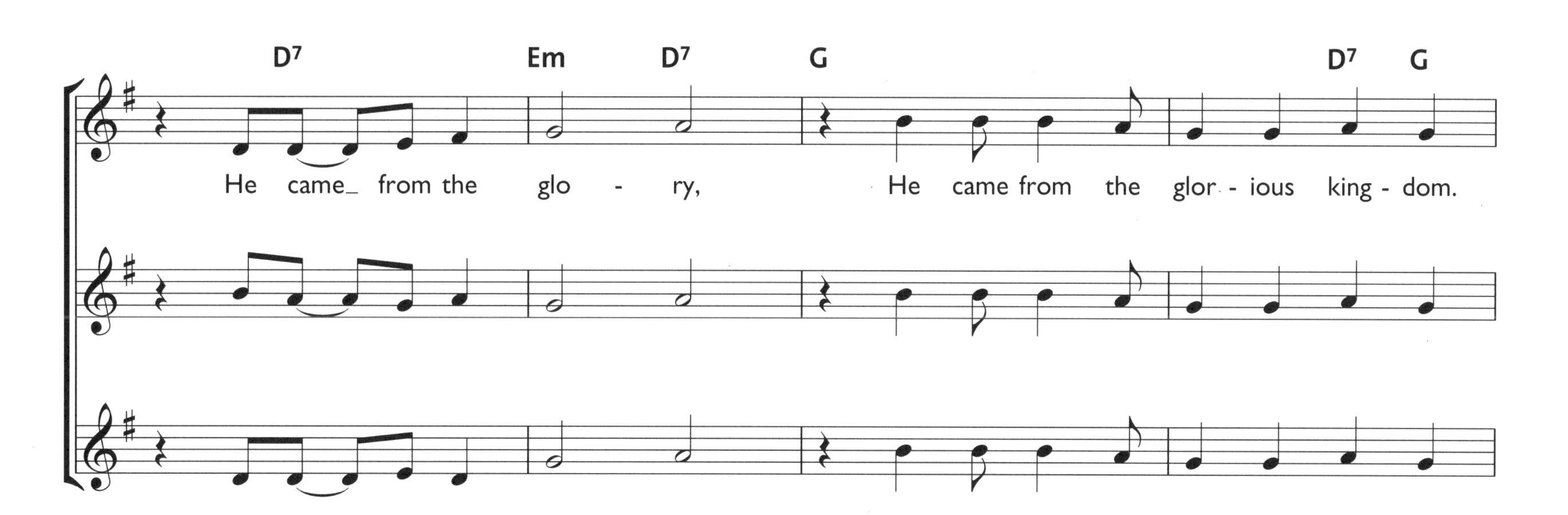
D7 Em D7 G D7 G
He came_ from the glo - ry, He came from the glor - ious king - dom.

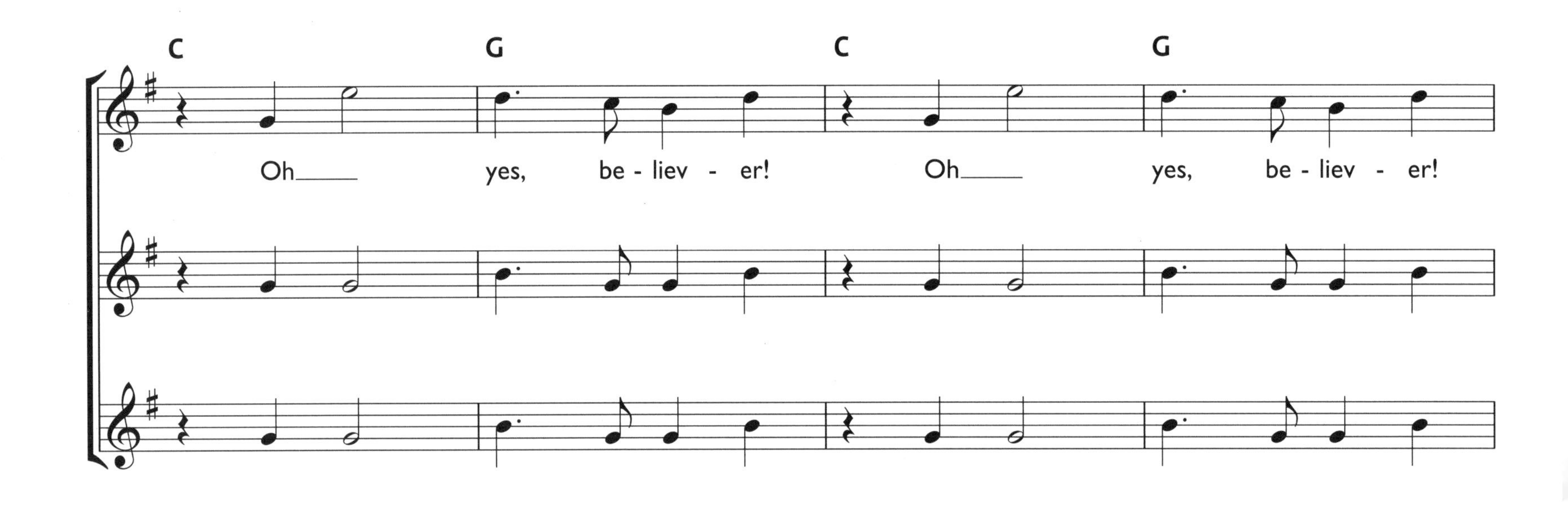
C
G
C
G
Oh___ yes, be - liev - er! Oh___ yes, be - liev - er!

D7
Em
D7
G
D7
G
He came_ from the glo - ry, He came from the glor - ious king - dom.

While Shepherds Watched

Words by Nahum Tate
Music: Traditional

CD Track 16
Intro: 4 bars
Link: 2 bars

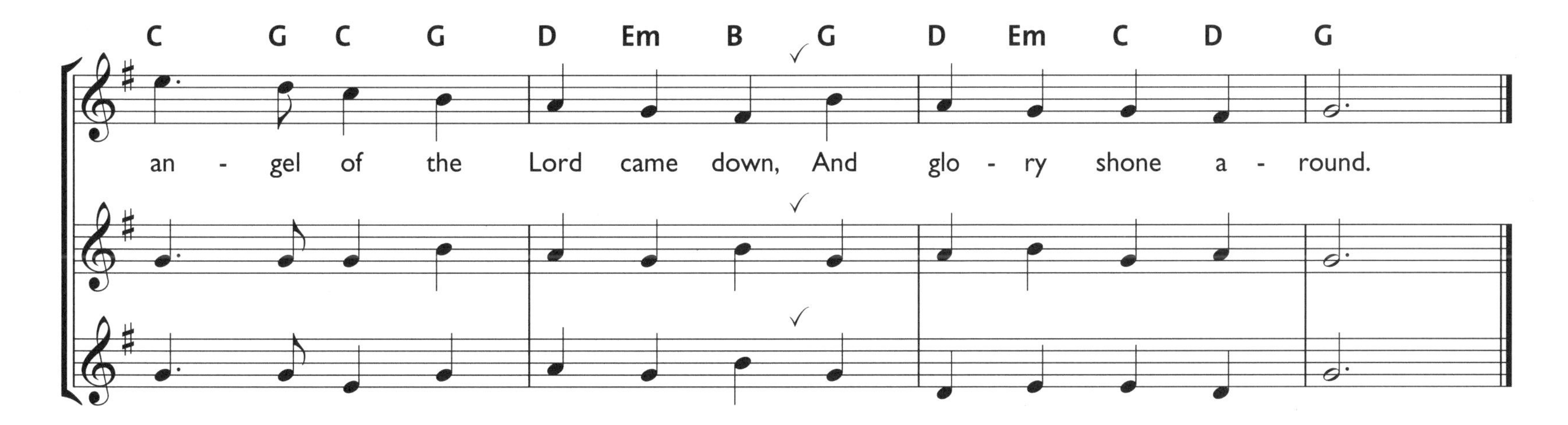

We Wish You A Merry Christmas

Traditional

CD Track 17
Intro: 4 bars
Link: 4 bars

G A7 D G D A7 D
tid - ings we bring to you and your kin. We

G D Em D D7 G C Am D7 G
wish you a Mer - ry Christ - mas and a Hap - py New Year!

Silent Night

Words by Joseph Mohr
Music by Franz Gruber

CD Track 18
Intro: 4 bars
Link: 2 bars

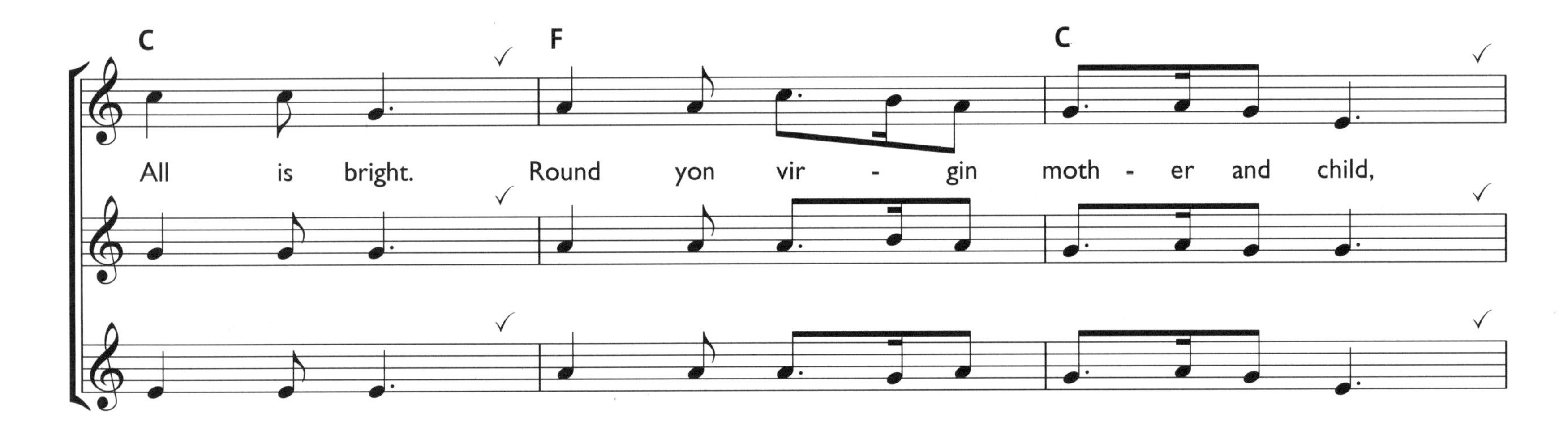

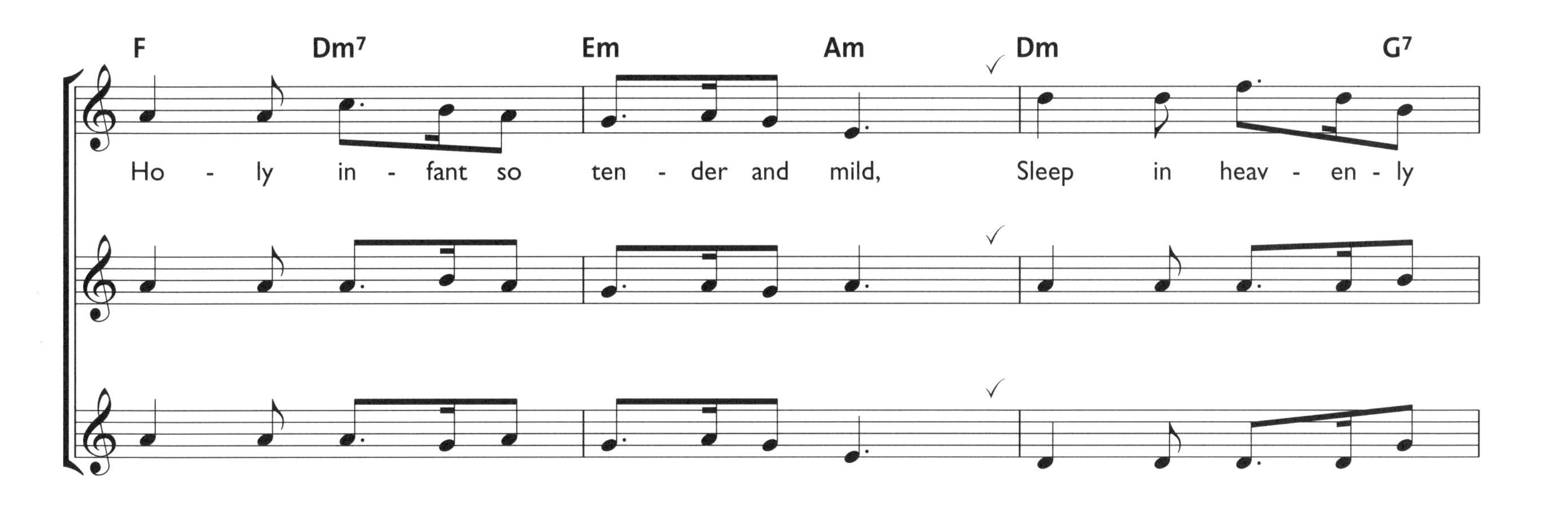
F
Dm7
Em
Am
Dm
G7
Ho - ly in - fant so ten - der and mild, Sleep in heav - en - ly

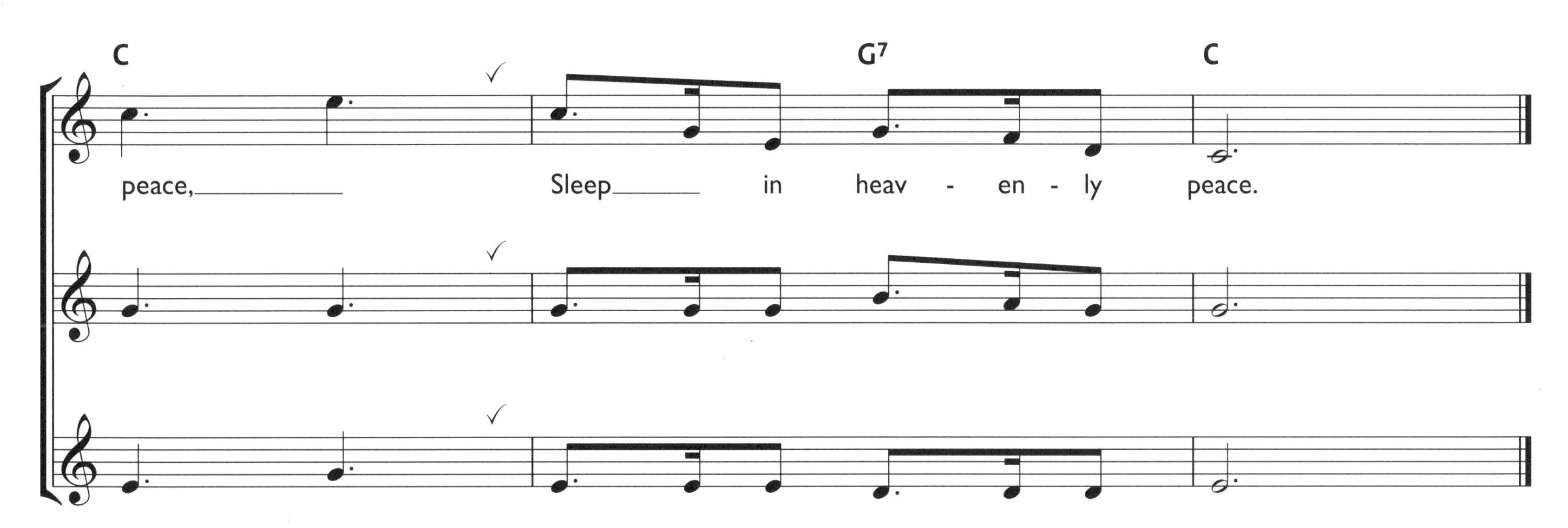
C
G7
C
peace, Sleep in heav - en - ly peace.

1 2 3 4 5 6 7 8 9